For Ann and Paul Krouse who have encouraged and supported this writer every step of the way, starting with my very first word: more. —A. K. R.

To Scotti Lichtenheld, the best mom a guy could hope for. —T. L.

ISBN 978-0-545-83520-6

12 11 10 9 8 7 6 5 4 3 2 15 16 17 18 19 20/0

Printed in Malaysia 108

First Scholastic printing, May 2015

Design by Sara Gillingham Studio

Typeset in Cabrito and Grenale

The illustrations in this book were rendered in ink, watercolor, pan pastels, and colored pencils, with digital art assistance from Kristen Cella.

I Wish You More

AMY KROUSE ROSENTHAL & TOM LICHTENHELD

SCHOLASTIC INC.

I wish you more ups

than downs.

I wish you more give than take.

I wish you more tippy-toes

than deep.

I wish you more we than me.

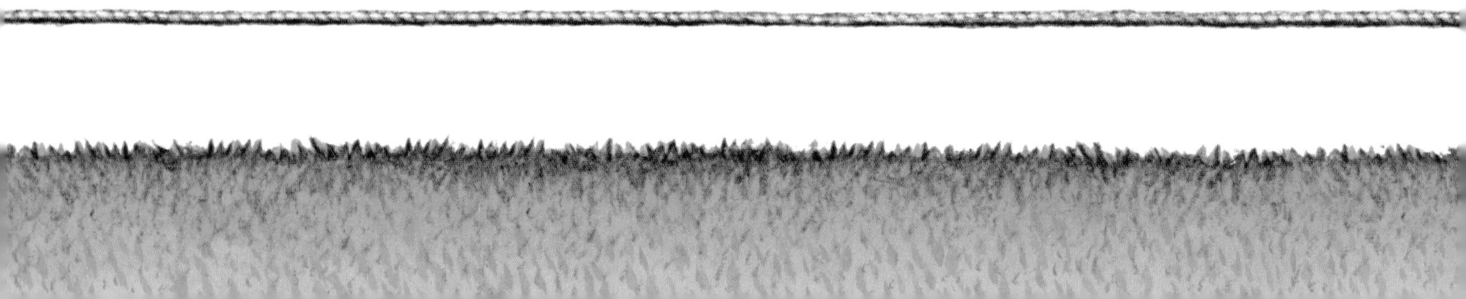

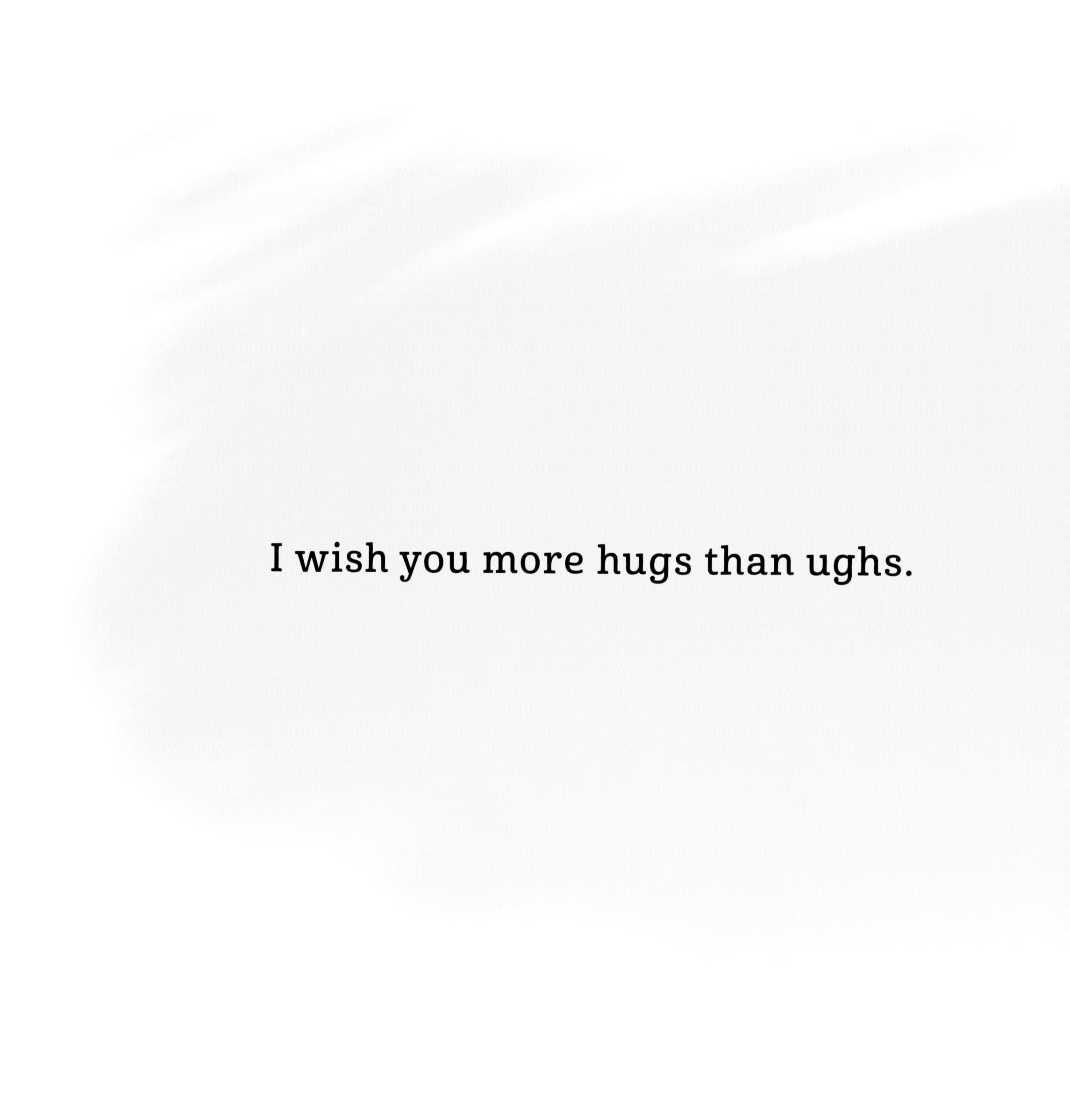
I wish you more hugs than ughs.

I wish you more WOO-HOO! than WHOA!

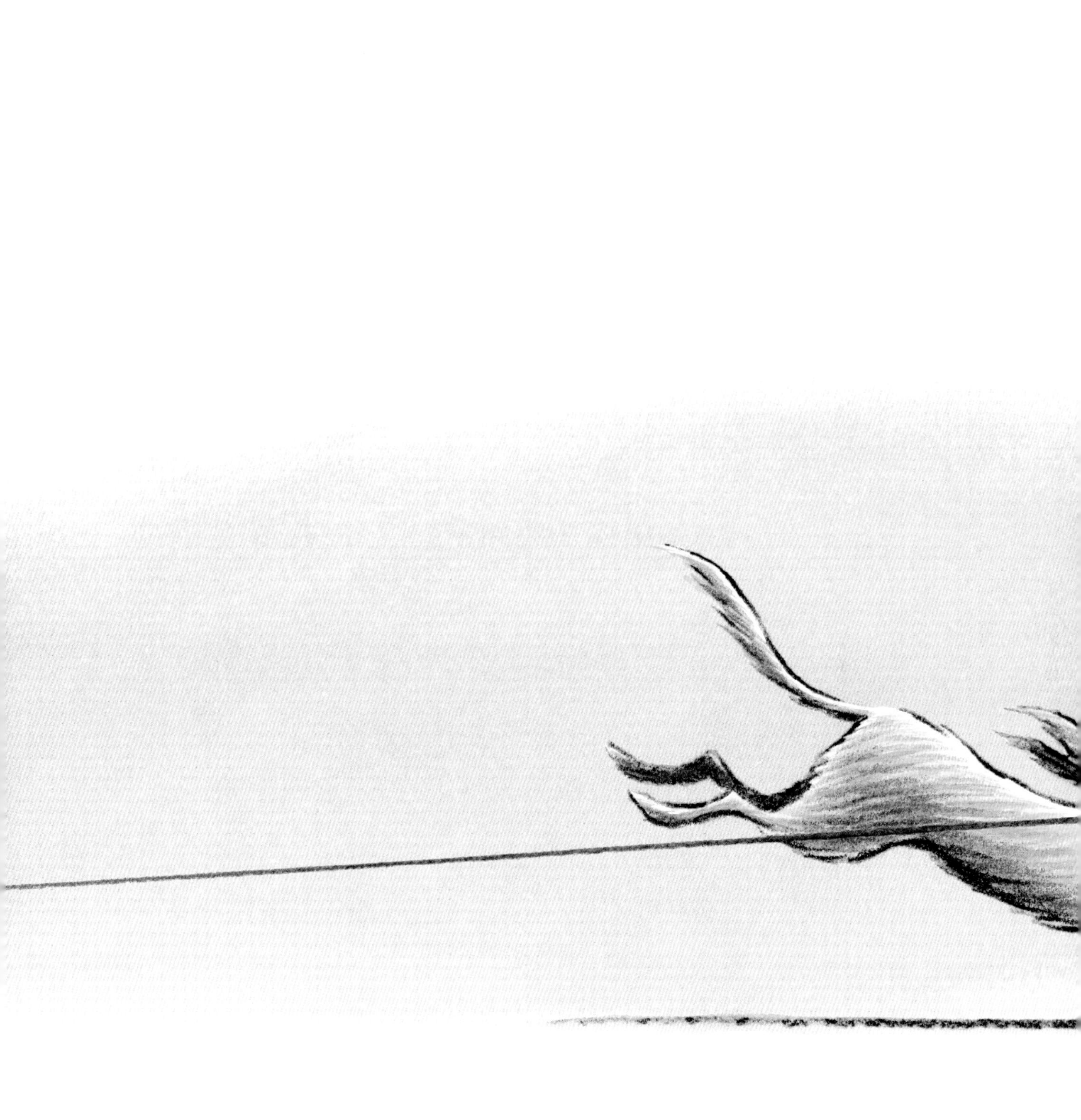

I wish you more will than hill.

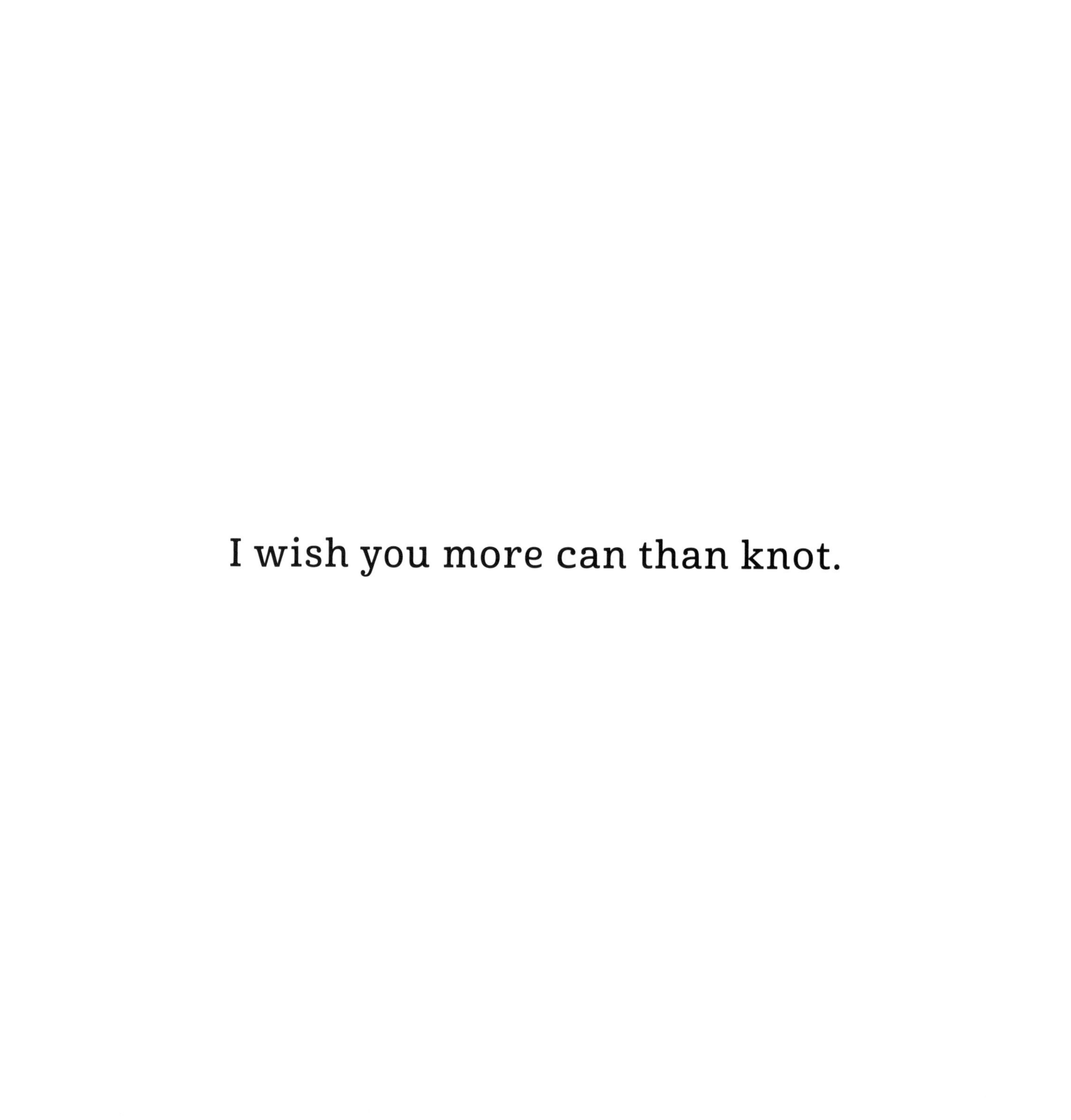
I wish you more can than knot.

I wish you more snowflakes

than tongue.

I wish you more pause

than fast-forward.

I wish you more umbrella than rain.

I wish you more bubbles than bath.

I wish you more treasures

than pockets.

I wish you more stories than stars.

I wish all of this for you,

because you are everything
I could wish for . . .

and more.